Running Water

Adam Stecher
Assistant Superintendent
Perth County Board of Education
Stratford, Ontario

Daniel F. Wentworth
Science Consultant
Hamilton Board of Education
Hamilton, Ontario

J. Kenneth Couchman
Co-ordinator of Programs, Junior Division
Hamilton-Wentworth Roman Catholic Separate School Board
Hamilton, Ontario

John C. MacBean
Science Consultant
Niagara South Board of Education
Port Colborne, Ontario

ISBN 0-03-922176-8

Distributed in the United States of America by
Mine Publications, Inc.,
25 Groveland Terrace,
Minneapolis, Minnesota 55403.

Published simultaneously in Great Britain by
Blond Educational Ltd.,
Iliffe House, Oadby, Leicestershire, England.

Printed in Canada 2 3 4 5 75

Running Water

Examining Your Environment

Adam Stecher

Daniel F. Wentworth

J. Kenneth Couchman

John C. MacBean

Holt, Rinehart and Winston of Canada, Limited.

Toronto Montreal

Contents

Introduction

Introduction

The photographs shown above provide two very different examples of running water. One shows the natural beauty of Niagara Falls with 500,000 tons of water per minute plunging over a precipice approximately 190 feet high. The other shows a tiny man-controlled stream dripping from a faucet or tap. A study of large quantities of running water such as found in streams and rivers is most interesting and useful, as many students have already discovered. Because small examples of running water, as illustrated by the dripping faucet, lack spectacular qualities and are so common, they are frequently overlooked. This book is written to make you more aware of the ordinary, everyday examples of running water found in the immediate vicinity of your home and school.

The polluted condition of many of our streams, rivers, lakes and seas and the scarcity of water in many areas are arousing serious concern throughout the world. It may appear to you, an individual student, that you have little personal control over these matters. As you do the investigations in *Running Water* your influence on the water supply and pollution may become somewhat clearer.

It is not necessary to have beforehand a great knowledge of running water in order to do the activities in this book. Nor do you need to have available a large number of reference books to assist you in finding answers. In fact, the answers to many of the problems can only be obtained by carrying out the activities. If you do them carefully, you will gather first-hand information about water in your own home and community.

Most of the suggested activities should be conducted outside, on or near the school grounds or in your yard. The equipment that is used can be easily obtained or readily made.

Try to work in groups. Before you start, plan carefully the jobs to be done, the equipment needed and the responsibility of each group member. Be certain to consider the way in which the data or information that you collect will be recorded. It may be necessary to prepare data sheets before you start the activity. Many activities should be repeated and the evidence obtained should be averaged. The care with which you do the activity and collect the data will determine your success in finding logical answers.

Do not feel that you must do all of the activities in this book. If one topic or chapter particulary interests you, you may wish to study it in greater depth and omit the other topics. As you work on the problems you may discover others that you want to investigate. Your problems may be much better than those suggested by the authors. Don't be afraid to investigate them.

After each problem is found a Digging Deeper section. This is designed to guide you toward a better understanding of the activity that you have completed and to assist you in interpreting the data that you have collected. The Branching Out suggestions provide starting points to investigations related to the problem that you have explored. You may find it interesting to pursue your own in-depth study of some of them.

Examining Your Environment
Other and Forthcoming Titles

Astronomy
Birds
The Dandelion
Ecology
Mapping Small Places
Mini-climates
Pollution
Small Creatures
Snow and Ice
Trees
Your Senses

Picture Credits

Cover photos: Ralph Campbell, *front;* J. Kenneth Couchman and Tom W. Hall, *back.*

J. A. Montgomery, *page vi left.*

Ralph Campbell
J. Kenneth Couchman
John C. MacBean
Adam Stecher
Daniel F. Wentworth

The Turning of a Tap

1. The Turning of a Tap

The turning of a tap is such a common experience that most of us take it very much for granted. We accept as our unquestioned right finger-tip access to unlimited quantities of fresh water. However, the days of wastefully indulging ourselves with this gift are coming to an end. Already severe shortages are being experienced in many parts of the world to the extent of even forcing rationing of water. In the not too distant future, we may come to regard turning on a tap as a cherished privilege to be diligently guarded by rigid conservation practices.

This chapter is written to better acquaint you with the water system in your house and school. As you examine pipes and faucets and carry out the suggested activities you will hopefully develop a greater appreciation of the luxury of instant water. You may be surprised to learn just how much you personally consume. Then, when you consider the millions of other people using similar quantities, the concern for the conservation of water may become more clear.

Activity 1:

What is the pathway of water in a building?

Choose one tap (faucet) in your home or school. Trace the path that fresh water takes to reach that tap and the path that waste water takes to leave.

Look under the sink and in the basement for clues. Ask your parents or the caretaker for assistance.

Visit a building that is under construction. Find the pathways of the water pipes that are being installed by the plumbers. Be sure to ask for permission.

Examine a blueprint of a house and find the water pathways.

Draw a plan of the fresh water and waste water pathway (the plumbing system) in your house or school. Use different colours to indicate the fresh and waste water pipes.

What is the most noticeable difference between fresh water pipes and waste water pipes?

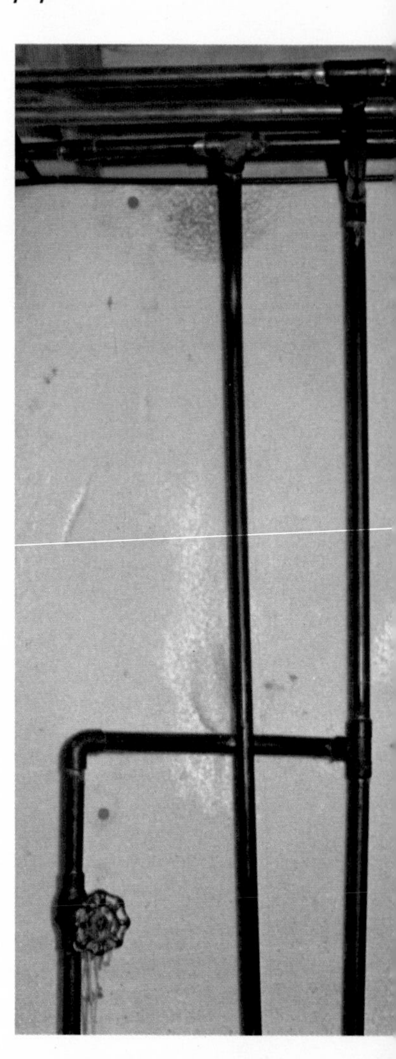

The plumbing system in most buildings will differ somewhat. How does your plan compare with this one?

Digging Deeper

How many water outlets are there in your house? school?

On what side of the sink is the hot water tap located?

How many different sizes (diameters) of pipe did you find?

What is the total length of all the piping in your house? school?

How much piping is there for hot water? cold water? How much piping is there for fresh water? waste water?

How are the taps and toilets in a building located to keep the amount of piping to a minimum?

What is the purpose of the vent that leads to the roof?

Branching Out

Obtain a map of your municipality from the city hall, a service station or a tourist information centre. Interview your city engineer to find:

(a) the pathway of fresh water from its source to your school,

(b) the waste water pathway from your school to where it finally enters a stream, lake or other body of water.

Mark these pathways on your map with bright colours.

Visit the local waterworks. You will undoubtedly have prepared many questions in advance of the visit. Be sure to include the following in your list:

What is the source of the local water supply — river, stream, lake, well?

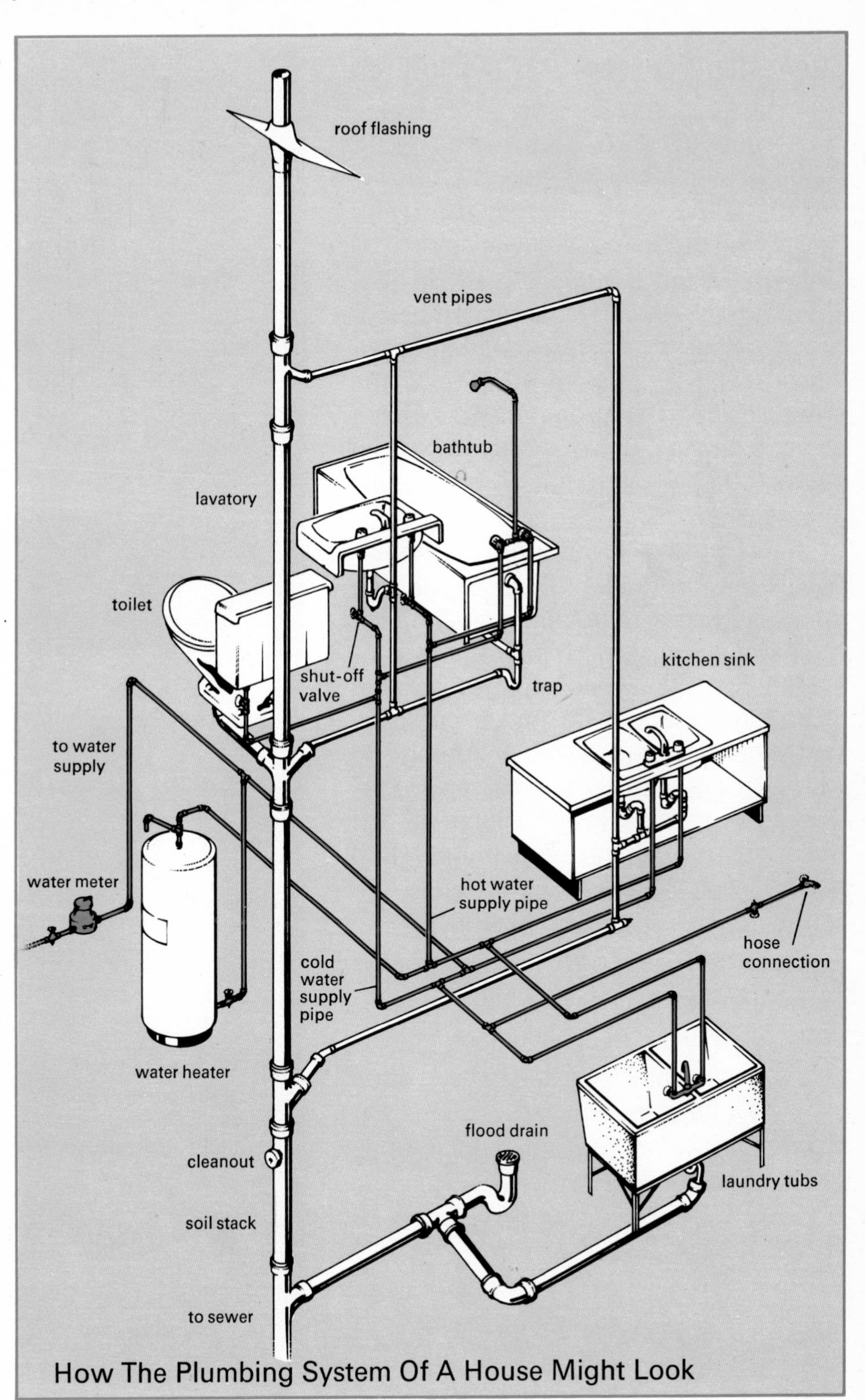

How The Plumbing System Of A House Might Look

What efforts are necessary to purify the water?

What quantity of water is used by your municipality on an average day?

What is the peak quantity of water used on a hot summer day?

Visit a sewage treatment plant to discover how waste water is treated before being released to rivers, streams or lakes. What volume of sewage is the plant designed to process? How much sewage does the plant process on an average day? How much does it handle at a peak?

In some areas even though the homes have running water, they cannot be connected to a municipal sewage system. Instead a *septic tank system* is installed. Use the yellow pages in your telephone directory to find a company that installs septic systems. Arrange to visit a home where the company is installing a septic system. Some of the questions to which you might find answers are:

How does a septic system work?

How large should the tank be?

What length of tile is needed?

How deeply are the tiles placed?

How is the tank emptied? How often should it be emptied?

Draw a map showing the house, tank, connecting pipes and the tiles. Read an

A local water pumping station.

The circular primary sedimentation tanks of a sewage treatment plant.

article about septic systems in an encyclopedia. How does this information compare with what you learned on your field trip?

Visit a home where a septic system has been operating for several years.

Interview the home owners to find what problems they have encountered or might encounter through using a septic system. Observe the tiled area for signs of where the tiles have been laid.

As cities expand the municipal sewage system reaches homes that have been using a septic system. What would be the cost to the home owner to have his house connected to the municipal sewage system? (The city engineer can assist with this question).

Observe the cold water pipes in your basement on a humid summer day. Why are they dripping water even though the pipes do not leak? (You can get a clue by looking at the outside of a glass of ice water which has been left standing for several minutes.)

THE WATER METER

Find the water meter in your house and examine its face. How does the face of the water meter compare with the face of a clock? What unit is used to measure the quantity of water that has been used? Some meters measure in gallons and others in cubic feet. How many gallons of water are there in one cubic foot? Turn on several taps. How many seconds does it take for 10 gallons of water to pass through the water meter?

Which pipe carries cold water?

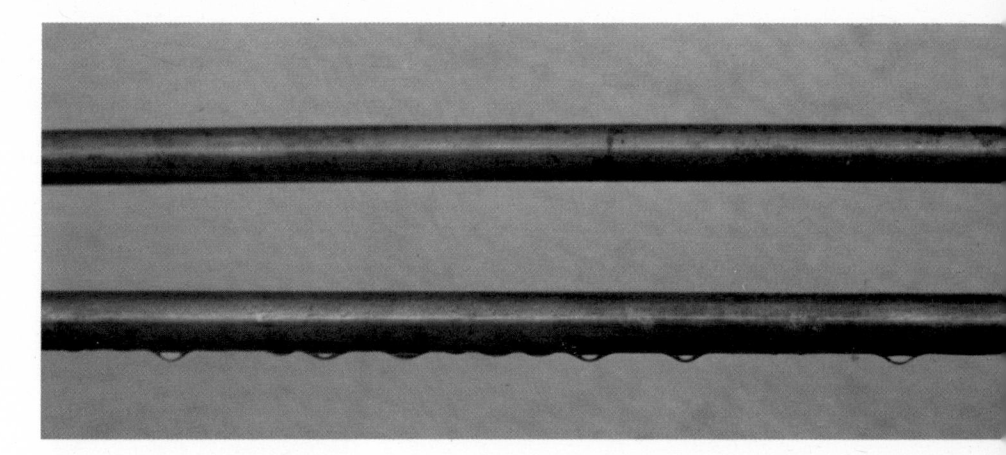

Why is the water meter found inside of a building?

WATER RATES

1st or Minimum Rate: $3.33 per month gross, up to and including 1000 gallons, less 10% Prompt Payment Discount.

2nd Rate: $0.55 gross per 1000 gallons for balance of consumption, less 10% Prompt Payment Discount.

Water Bills Issued Every Four Months

(Minimum 4 Month Bill—Gross $13.32, Net $11.99)

Schedule of Net Monthly Rates

WATER

	Cost Per 100 Cubic Feet (Cu. Ft.)
First 500 cu. ft.	36c
Next 9500 " "	18c
Over 10000 " "	12c
Monthly service charge	60c
Minimum Monthly Consumption charge	$1.10

Sewage Charge —

⅔ of Water Consumption charge

Here are samples of the water rates of two municipalities located quite close to each other. Which municipality has the lower cost of water? Calculate the cost of water in each municipality if 8,000 gallons are used in the month.

Examine the water bill for your house. How much does water cost? How does this cost compare with other municipalities? Why is the cost of water reduced when greater quantities are used? Who determines how much water will cost? What are some of the things that might affect the cost of water?

How much water do you use? Read the meter to find how many gallons of water are used in your school in an average week. (Take the average for three weeks). Calculate the number of gallons of water per person used in your home in a day.

In some communities that provide a water supply there are no water meters. Each householder pays a *flat rate*. This means that he is charged a set amount regardless of the quantity of water consumed. What disadvantages, particularly from a conservation viewpoint, can you see in this system?

THE TOILET

Ask an adult to remove the lid of a toilet tank and demonstrate how the water in the tank is released and how the tank is again filled.

How is the water turned on? Trace the pathway of the water into the tank.

How is the water turned off?

What is the purpose of the float tank ball?

Why does the tank ball float even though it is made of metal?
How can the toilet be shut off from the rest of the water system?
How much water does the tank hold?

THE CONVENIENCE OF A PLUMBING SYSTEM

Try to imagine your house without a plumbing system now that you have become accustomed to the unrestricted use of water. In many areas people still rely on the well and pump for their water supply. During the summer droughts the municipal water supply sometimes fails and it is necessary to have drinking water delivered by a water truck.

The flush tank of a toilet.

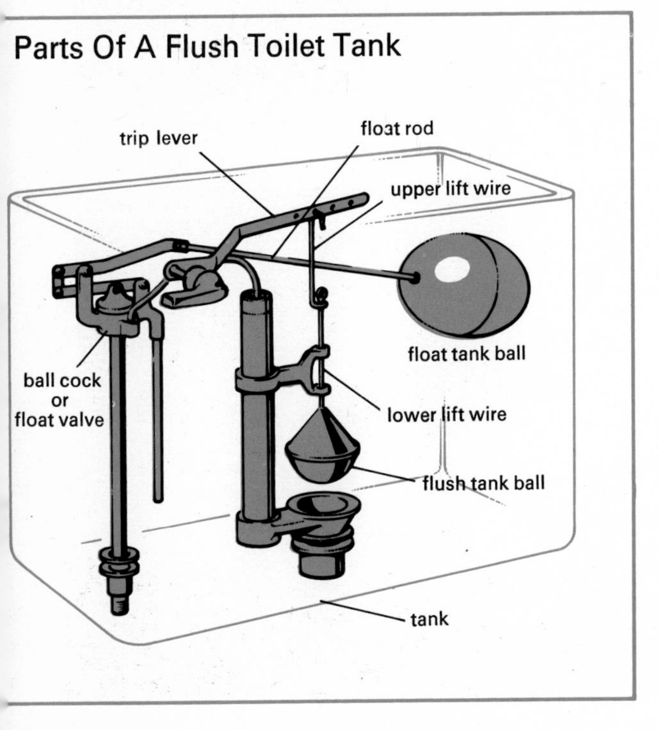

The compression tap. There are many varieties or styles of taps. How similar are the taps that you examined to this one?

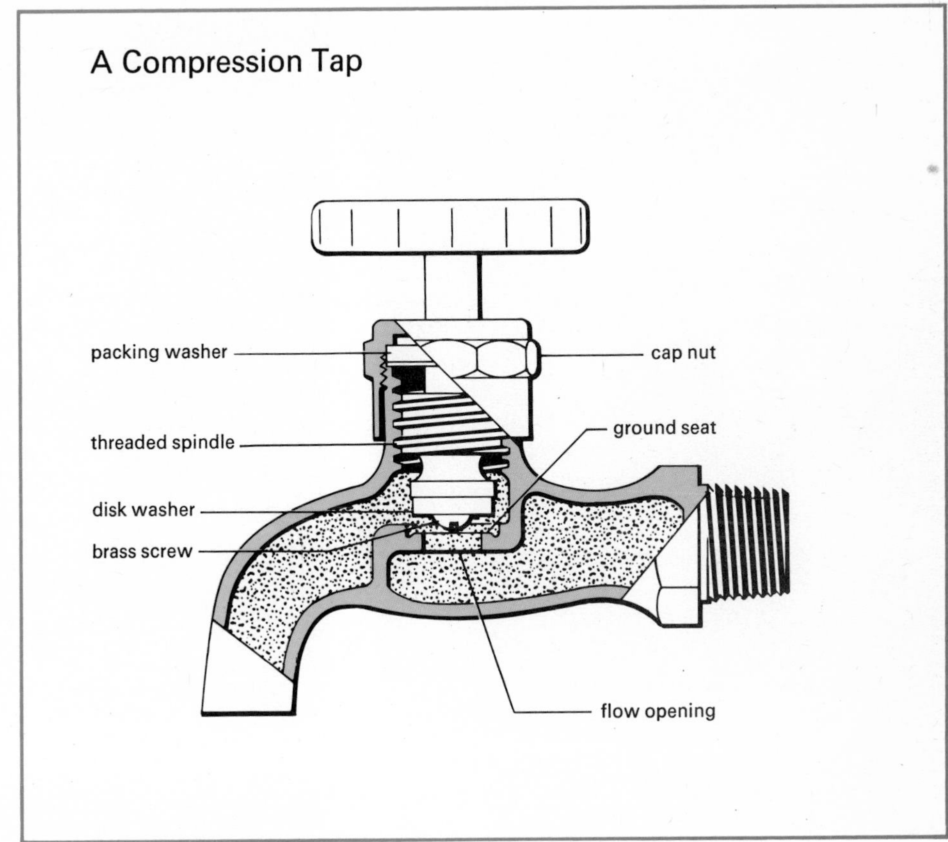

Using the headings time, labour, cleanliness, health and cost, write a composition describing the advantages of a reliable indoor water supply.

Activity 2:

What is a tap?

Obtain some old taps from a plumber or from your home.
Take the taps apart. You will need a screwdriver and an open-end wrench or a monkey wrench. With the help of the diagram label each part.

We might consider this a primitive method of obtaining our water supply. How might an aborigine of the Kalahari Desert in Africa respond to a water supply such as provided by a water truck?

Many people still rely on a hand operated pump and well for their water supply.

The parts of a compression tap or faucet.

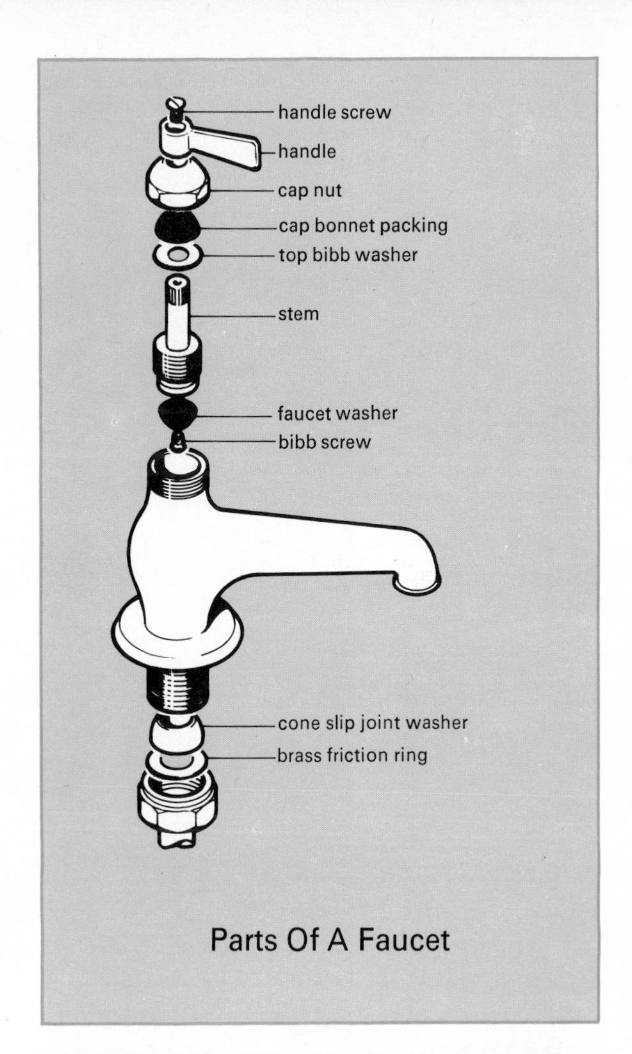

Parts Of A Faucet

Put the taps together again and connect them to a length of garden hose so that they can be tested.

Digging Deeper

What purpose does a tap serve?
Which parts move to make an opening through which water can flow?
Which parts help to prevent leaks?

Branching Out

FIXING FAUCETS

Most houses have *compression* taps (the type shown in the diagram). A washer moves up and down over a *seat* or opening to control the flow of water. Compression taps develop two common types of leaks.

(a) Dripping from beneath the handle. This is caused by worn packing.

(b) Dripping from the spout. This is usually caused by a worn washer.

Try to repair a leaky tap. It will be necessary to have washers and packing on hand. Remember to replace the worn washer with one the same size.

WASTING WATER

Many houses have leaky taps that should be repaired. How much water is wasted by leaky taps? Find a leaky tap in your house or school. Collect all the water that escapes from the tap over a 24-hour period. How much water was wasted by the one tap in one day? How much would it waste in a year? Make a reasonable guess as to the amount of

Did your tap work properly after you re-assembled it?

water that might be wasted each day in your town if every tap leaked the same amount.

Some people carelessly neglect to completely turn off a tap. Look around your house for taps that have been left running. Estimate how much water can be wasted in one day by a tap left running slowly.

What telltale evidence can you find in sinks where taps have been leaking or left dripping over a long period of time?

TYPES OF TAPS

Find and display samples and pictures of different styles of taps. Although taps vary greatly in appearance and price most of them work on the same principle. How many styles of taps can you find in your house and school? Examine a tap that permits hot and cold water to be mixed at any desired temperature. How does it work?

TURN-OFF VALVES

Most houses have one or more faucets on the outside of the house. These are used when watering the lawn or for similar purposes. Just inside the basement wall, next to the tap, is a turn-off valve. Why is the turn-off valve placed there?

Look in the basement, beside the water meter, for the turn-off valve. When might this valve be used?

Look on the lawn or driveway for the water turn-off valve. When might this valve be used?

Is this a turn-off valve? In what places would you expect to find a turn-off valve?

This picture shows only a small range of pipes. Try to find others made of different materials.

Difference in Pipes				
Pipe	Inside Diameter	Thickness of Wall	Material of which pipe is made	Purpose for which pipe is used
A				
B				
C				
D				

Activity 3:

How are pipes different?

Examine as many pipes as possible. Look at pipes in the school, bring samples from home, and visit a plumbing supply shop.

Make a chart of the differences that you find in the pipes. You could use the following outline to help with your record.

What other differences in pipes did you discover?

Digging Deeper

What was the largest diameter of pipe that you found? For what was it used?

What is the most common diameter of pipe used in your house?

How does the thickness of the material in the wall of a small diameter pipe compare with that in the wall of a large diameter pipe?

Is there any relationship between the diameter of a pipe and the use of the pipe?

What is the longest length of pipe that you found?

What was the material most frequently used in making water pipes?

What differences can you find between pipes used in houses built 50 years ago and those built recently? What problem frequently arises in old water pipes that have been carrying *hard* water?

Some pipes used in the construction of a sewer system.

Branching Out

The following questions will require some reading to find the answers. Ask your librarian to help you locate good reference books.

On a map of the country show the path of the major oil and gas pipelines. How long are the oil and gas pipelines? What is the greatest pipe diameter used? Of what material are these pipes made?

What plans have been prepared to ship solid materials such as coal by pipeline? Where are cement pipes usually used?

The early Romans had a highly sophisticated water distribution system. Most of their pipes were made of lead. Why did they use this metal? What dangers are encountered in using lead pipes to carry drinking water?

Activity 4:

How does the pressure (force of water) coming from a tap vary?

Attach a hose and nozzle to an outside tap and turn the tap on full. All other taps should be turned off.

Open the nozzle to its full opening and measure the distance that the water travels. The nozzle should be held parallel to the ground at waist height. It is important that the nozzle be held the same way throughout the activity. Why? If you cannot hold the nozzle steady, it can be tied to a chair in order to maintain a constant position.

Have someone turn on a second tap somewhere in the building. Again measure the distance that the water travels from the nozzle of the hose.

Measure the distance again after a third, fourth and fifth tap have been turned on.

Measuring the distance that water travels from a nozzle.

On a line graph, similar to the one below, show the distances that the water travelled.

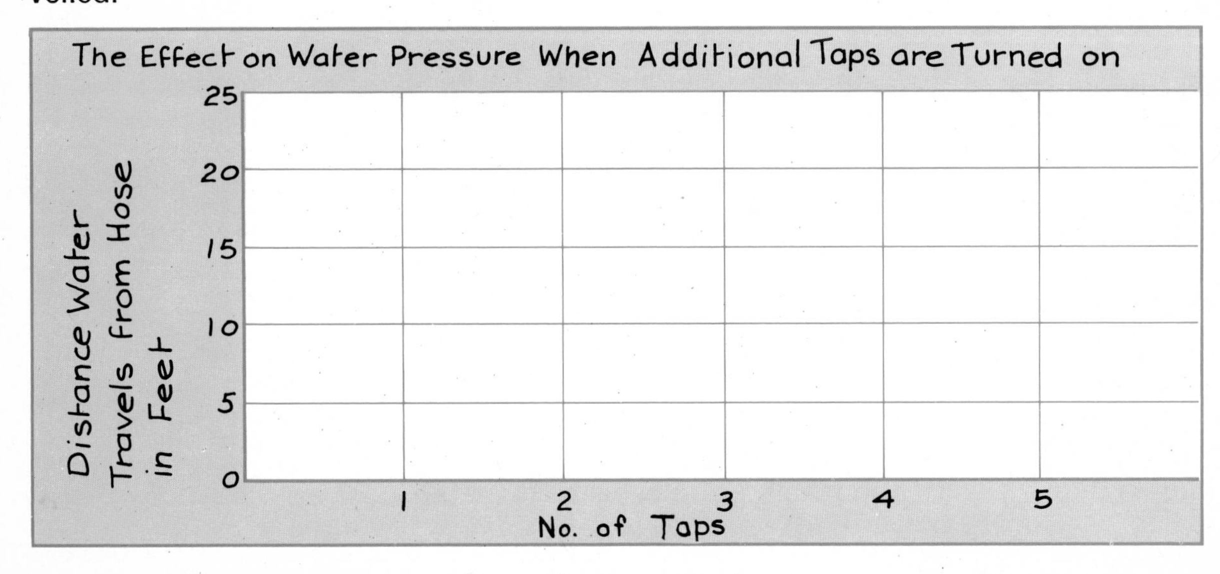

Digging Deeper

What was the greatest distance that the water travelled? the shortest?

What happens to the distance the water travels as more taps are turned on?

What causes this change? How can this change be explained in terms of water pressure?

Would the results be different if the additional taps that were turned on were on the second or third floor of the building? in the basement?

Explain why water can suddenly turn cold when you are taking a shower if someone turns on the hot water tap in the basement.

On hot summer days people in some communities find that when a tap is turned on little or no water comes out. What is the probable cause of this inconvenience?

How does the pressure of water coming from a hose change when the tap handle is turned clockwise? counterclockwise? What causes these changes in water pressure?

Try to hold back the water from a hose with your thumb. How successful are you?

Branching Out

Repeat the steps of Activity 4 but flush a toilet instead of turning on a second tap. Compare the effect of flushing a toilet and turning on another tap on water pressure.

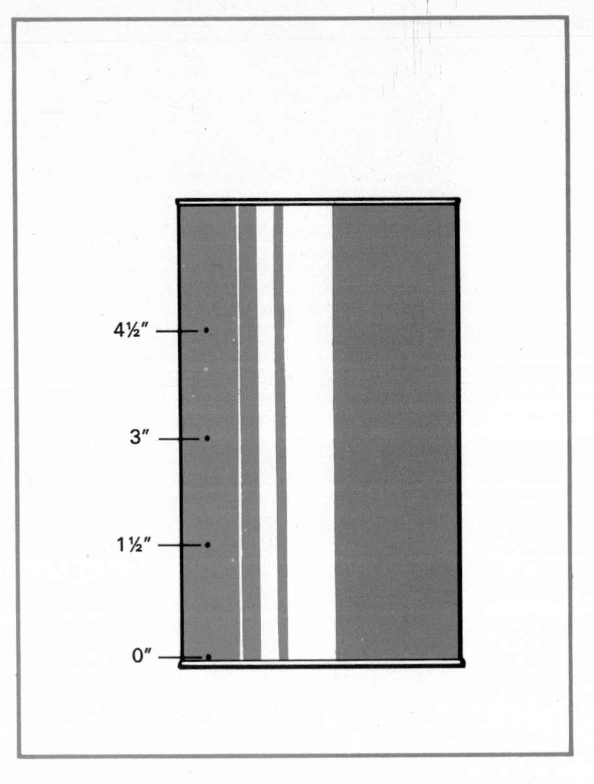

Punch holes in a quart-size oil can at the heights shown. How tall is a quart-size oil can? If it is tapped gently with a hammer, a 2½ inch finishing nail will make a hole quite easily.

With a nail, at the heights shown, punch holes in the oil can.

Keep the oil can continually filled with a watering can or hose. It doesn't matter if some water runs over the top.

Measure the horizontal distance that the water spurts from each hole.

Show your findings on a line graph.

How does the distance that the water spurts from the holes at 3 inches and 0 inches compare? How does the water pressure at the 3 inch point compare with the water pressure at 0 inches?

How does the distance that the water spurts from the hole at 0 inches compare with the height of the water in the can?

How far might the water from the hole at 0 inches spurt if the height of the water in the can was 100 feet?

With a nail, punch two holes in a quart-size oil can at the 1 inch level.

Keep the oil can continually filled with a watering can or hose.

Measure the horizontal distance that the water spurts from each hole.

Obtain an oil can and punch two holes 1 inch from the bottom of the can.

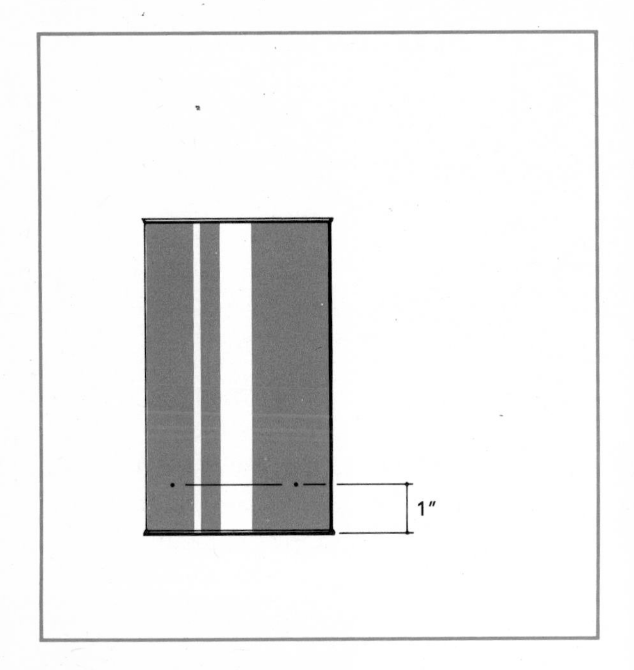

Make an additional hole at the 1 inch mark and again measure the distance that the water spurts.
Account for the answer that you found. Predict the distance that water would spurt from each hole if six holes were made at the 1 inch level. Test your prediction to discover whether or not you are right.
Visit your local water pumping station. Find out at what pressure the water is pumped through the water mains.

Find a water tower in your locality. How much water does it hold? How high is the water tower? How does the height of the water tower compare with the height of buildings in the vicinity? Explain how the water tower provides pressure in the pipes.

The water tower provides a reservoir of water for immediate use.

How would you explain the manner in which water spurts from each can?

Activity 5:

What can we learn about fire hydrants?

Count and measure as many of the parts of a fire hydrant as possible.

These could include:
(a) the diameter of the pipes and caps,
(b) the size of the nuts,
(c) the height and width,
(d) the links on the chains.

Compare several fire hydrants. How are they alike? different?

In what ways must all fire hydrants be alike? Why?

Ask a fireman to turn on a fire hydrant.

Find out how the hydrant is used in a fire emergency.

Find the answers to the following questions. The fireman would be a helpful resource person.

Why are fire hydrants painted bright colours such as red or yellow?

Who is allowed to use a fire hydrant?

How does water get to the fire hydrant?

How much water can come out of the hydrant?

How much does a fire hydrant cost?

What purpose do the chains serve?

Examine the lettering on a hydrant to find who made the hydrant and when and where it was made.

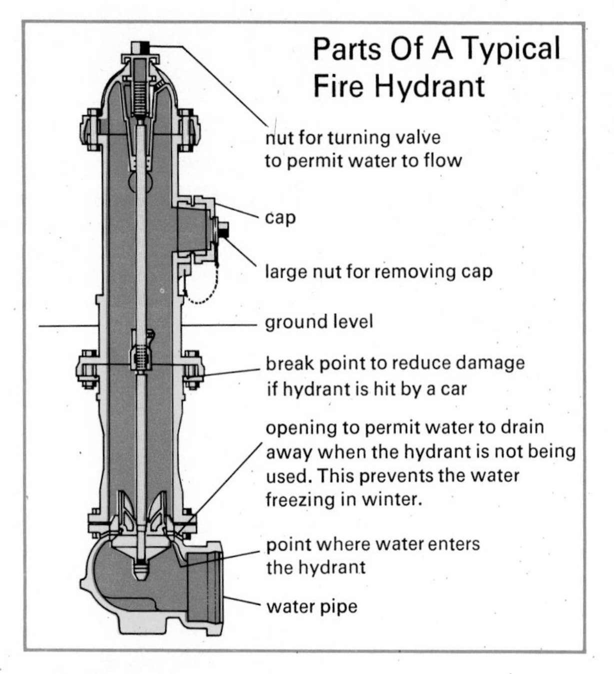

The insides of a typical fire hydrant.

Digging Deeper

How far apart are fire hydrants?

How close to your school is a fire hydrant?

Calculate the greatest distance between a house and the closest fire hydrant in your school area.

Ask a fire insurance salesman what effect the presence of fire hydrants has on house insurance rates in your area.

Branching Out

How does the type of fire extinguisher shown in the picture work?
For what type of fire would the fire extinguisher shown in the picture be used?

How many other types of fire extinguishers can you find? When would you use each type?

Sprinklers, Hoses and Nozzles

2. *Sprinklers, Hoses and Nozzles*

During the summer many people find that it is desirable to assist the normal rainfall. Lawns and gardens profit greatly from irrigation (watering) by means of hoses and sprinklers. When we water our lawns and gardens we are actually producing a controlled rainfall in a particular area.

Who can resist playing with water, particularly when it is associated with sprinklers, hoses and nozzles? The following activities can provide an opportunity for fun as well as learning. They will make you more familiar with irrigation around your house and school and also produce a better understanding of rainfall.

Activity 1:

In what ways are garden hoses different?

Bring to school as large a variety of garden hoses as possible.

Examine these hoses and others both at your home and at the hardware store.

Note as many differences as you can find. The information that you gather can be recorded on a chart similar to the one shown.

What other differences did you discover?

What tests for flexibility can you suggest?

Digging Deeper

What was the largest inside diameter of hose? the smallest? the most common?

Of what material were most hoses made?

How long was the longest hose? the shortest?

What type of hose was most expensive? least expensive?

Which hose is considered to be the best? Why? The man at the hardware store can help you with this question.

In what ways can hoses be connected to make them longer?

Branching Out

Examine other hoses, such as those

Differences in Garden Hoses

Garden Hose	Material of which it is made	Inside Diameter	Outside Diameter	Length	Flexibility
A					
B					
C					

How many different kinds of hoses can be found on this pumper?

used to irrigate a golf course, the fire hose at your school, the hoses on fire trucks, hoses in a car, etc. to find further differences in hoses.

Activity 2:

How does the inside diameter of a hose affect the quantity of water that can pass through it?

Select hoses that have different inside diameters. If possible, the length of hose and the material of which they are made should be the same.

Connect each hose, one at a time, to the same tap.

After the hose is connected, turn the tap on full each time.

Use the second hand on a watch or a stopwatch to time the flow of water into a pail for exactly 10 seconds.

Use a pint sealer or a measuring cup to measure the number of pints of water that came from each hose.

Repeat the activity letting the water from each hose run into the pail for 20 seconds.

Place your information on a chart and then on a graph.

Measuring the quantity of water that passes through a hose.

Digging Deeper

The inside diameter of a ¾ inch hose is one half greater than the inside diameter of a ½ inch hose. Was the flow of water one half times greater from the ¾ inch hose than from the ½ inch hose?

Water Flow from Hoses with Different Inside Diameters

Hose	Inside Diameter	Pints of Water in 10 seconds	Pints of Water in 20 seconds
A			
B			
C			

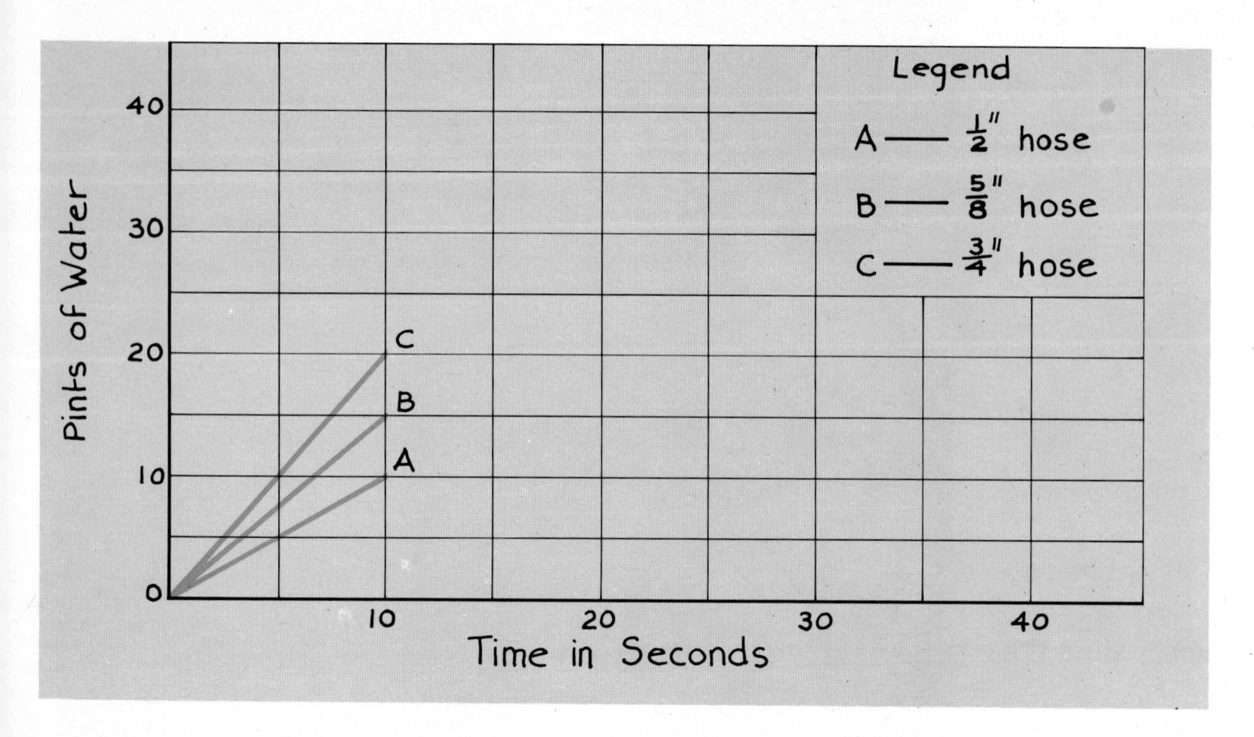

How can you explain the difference in your answer?

When using the ½ inch hose, how does the amount of water collected compare for the 10 second and the 20 second periods?

Predict how much water could flow from the ¾ inch hose in 30 seconds. Test your answer.

Predict how much water can flow from the ½ inch hose in 15 seconds. Use your graph to help you arrive at an answer.

Repeat the activity for measuring the flow of water from the hoses using different lengths of time and plot your data on the graph. If the experiment is properly controlled why is it logical to expect the line on the graph for each hose to be a straight, slanted line? How would the line be affected if one reading was taken while another tap in the house was running?

Express the flow of water from each hose in pints per second and in gallons per minute.

Branching Out

Find the rate of flow of other hoses such as fire hoses. This information can best be obtained by asking the person who uses the hose.

Does the length of a hose or the material of which a hose is made affect the quantity of water passing through it? Plan and do an experiment to find out.

The device should be anchored by stones so that it will not be knocked over by the force of the water.

Activity 3:

What affects the force of water coming from a nozzle?

Construct a device like the one shown in the diagram.

Connect a hose and nozzle to a tap and turn the tap on full. The nozzle should be adjusted to produce the most powerful stream of water possible.

How can this be determined?

Hold the nozzle at distances of 5 feet, 10 feet and 15 feet from the device.

Aim the nozzle so that the stream of water strikes the flap. For each distance record the maximum angle to which the wooden flap can be pushed by the stream of water.

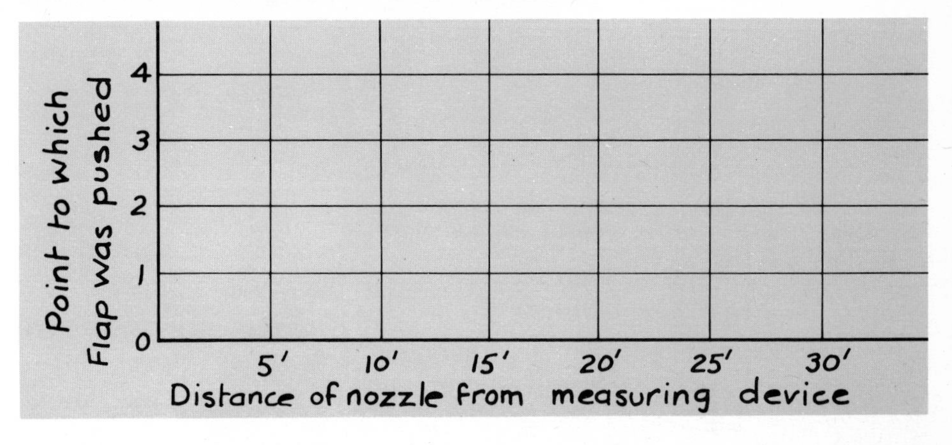

Digging Deeper

At what distance was the flap pushed least? most?

What effect does distance have on the force of the water?

What kind of stream of water pushed the flap the farthest (a gentle stream or a hard stream)?

Note the area (amount of surface) on the flap that was hit by the stream of water at each distance. Was the area the same at 5 feet as it was at 15 feet?

Change the adjustment on the nozzle. Does the same quantity of water come from the nozzle? Test the force of the water and compare the results with your earlier results.

What are some of the factors that might affect the force of water flowing from a nozzle?

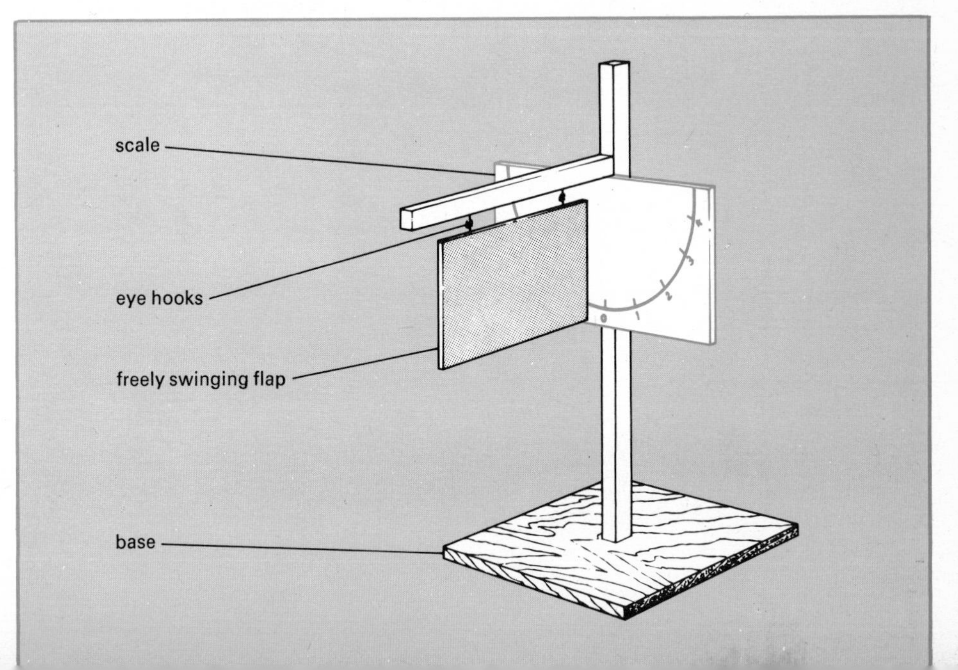

Branching Out

The force with which water flows from a hose is called pressure.

Refer to encyclopedias and other books in your library to find answers to these questions:

(a) How are *high pressure* hoses used in the mining industry?

(b) What is a *water cannon*?

Plan and do an experiment to discover how the adjustment of the nozzle affects the distance water will travel.

Remove the nozzle from the hose and place your thumb over the end of the hose. Experiment to find a method for making the water travel the greatest distance.

What is the purpose of a nozzle? How does it work?

From a distance of 15 feet water a piece of bare ground with a hose for a few minutes. Repeat the activity in exactly the same way except from a distance of 3 feet. Compare the effects on the ground surface. What does this reveal about the force of the water coming from a hose? Look for evidence of the effect of a hard driving rain on bare soil.

Activity 4:

In what different ways do lawn sprinklers spread water?

Obtain as many different types of lawn sprinklers as you can.

Attach each one, in turn, to a hose and observe the way in which the water is sprinkled.

Sketch and describe the sprinkling action of each type of sprinkler.

Digging Deeper

Find out how each different type of sprinkler works.

Activity 5:

How large a surface does a lawn sprinkler water?

Place a sprinkler, that is attached to a hose and tap, in the middle of a grassy area.

How many other sprinkling methods did you find?

Turn the tap on full and let the sprinkler operate for a few minutes.

Place large pebbles at regular intervals to enclose the area being watered by the sprinkler.

Turn off the sprinkler and measure the size of the area that was watered.

If the area that is watered is a rectangle measure the length and width.

If the area is a circle measure the distance from the sprinkler to the edge of the watered area. (This measurement is called the radius.)

Repeat these steps with each of the different sprinklers that are available.

Use the measurements that you have gathered to help you make a scale drawing on graph paper of the area watered by each sprinkler.

Digging Deeper

Which sprinkler spread water over the largest area? the smallest?

Do you think that approximately the same quantity of water comes from each sprinkler? How could you test your answer? (Hint: Try using the method suggested in Activity 2.)

Which sprinkler would likely have to be moved most frequently when watering the lawn? Why?

Calculate, in square feet, the area covered by each sprinkler. Compare the results.

You have found that the area watered by different sprinklers is not the same. In what situations might each sprinkler best be used?

Finding the area that is watered by a sprinkler. Why are the stones placed at the edge of the watered area?

Why would the kinds of sprinklers normally used on lawns be impractical on a golf course?

Branching Out

Visit a golf course and find the area covered by the large sprinklers.

How do truck farmers irrigate their crops?

Carry out an experiment to find how deeply each sprinkler waters the ground in ½ hour? in 1 hour? in 1½ hours? in 2 hours?

When watering a lawn in the summer which watering system is best, watering daily for 10 minutes or watering once a week for 1 hour? Explain your answer.

Perhaps you have found that you can control the area that a sprinkler can water by turning down the tap. What effect has this on the quantity of water that is spread? If the tap was adjusted so that only half as much water as possible flowed, would the area covered by the sprinkler be half as great as when the tap was on full?

HOW TO MAKE A SIMPLE RAIN GAUGE

The amount of water that falls during a rain is often very difficult to measure because it is so small. A rainfall of 1/16 inch or less is quite common. If you tried to measure this small quantity there would be a strong possibility of error. To make the measurement of rainfall easier a simple rain gauge can be used. This device can also be used to measure the quantity of water dispersed by a sprinkler.

Obtain a tobacco can and a tall narrow bottle such as an alka-seltzer bottle.

Pour exactly ¼ inch of water into the tobacco can. This can be done quite

The ¼ inch of rain collected in the tobacco can is easily measured when poured into the alka-seltzer bottle. Practise measuring small quantities of water with your rain gauge.

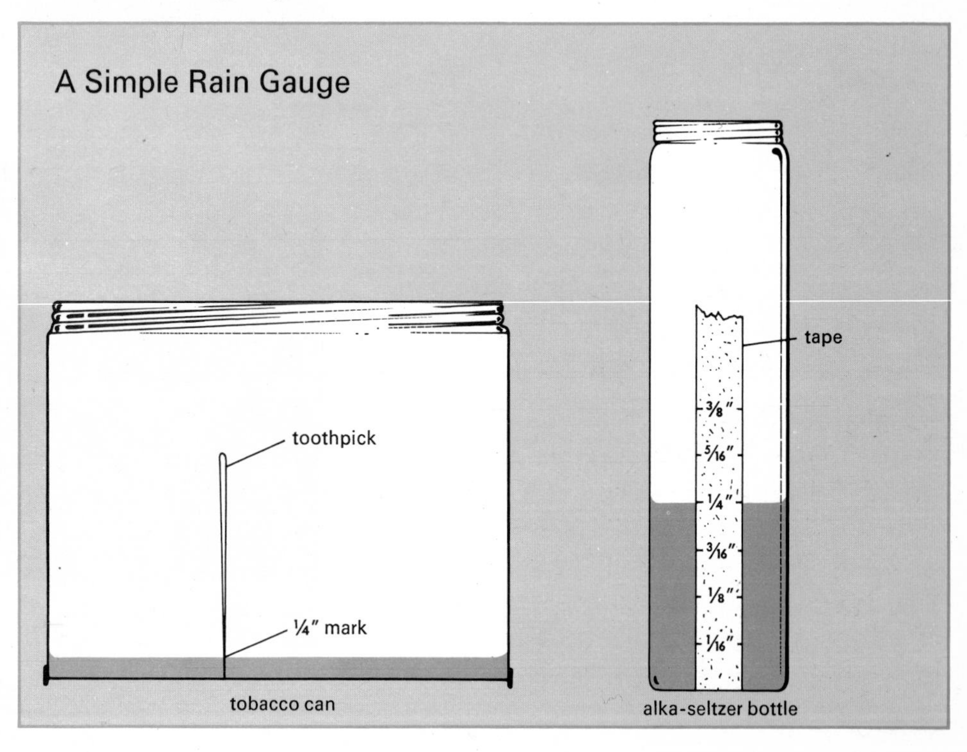

easily by placing a ¼ inch mark on a toothpick. Hold the toothpick upright in the can and add water drops until the ¼ inch level is reached.

Place a piece of masking tape lengthwise on the alka-seltzer bottle.

Pour the water from the can into the bottle.

Mark the water level on the masking tape and label it ¼". Half the distance from the bottom of the bottle would represent ⅛ inch of rainfall.

Place marks on the masking tape to show 1/16", ⅛", 3/16", 5/16", ⅜".

To use this device, the tobacco can is placed outside to collect rain. The water collected is then poured into the alka-seltzer bottle and can thus be measured with great accuracy.

Activity 6:

How evenly does a sprinkler spread water?

Set a sprinkler in an open area such as a lawn.

Place several tobacco cans (the same size) in various places around the sprinkler so that they can catch the water from the sprinkler.

Turn on the sprinkler and let it run for an hour.

Use a narrow bottle such as an alka-seltzer bottle that has been properly gauged to measure the amount of water collected by each can.

Prepare a map of the area being watered and on it record the quantity of water collected at each location of a tobacco can.

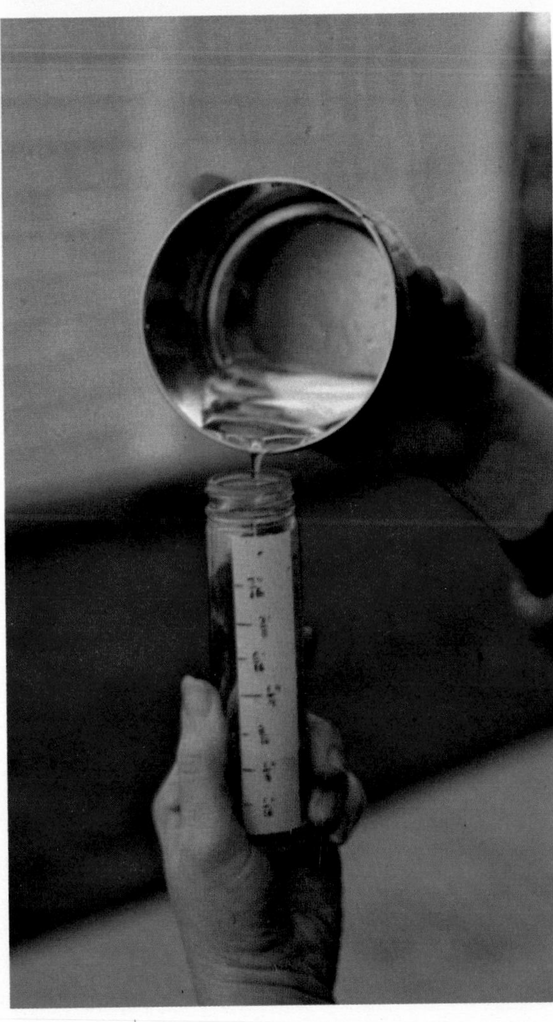

The tobacco cans should be placed so that you get a fair representation of the entire area being watered. Try various patterns for placing the cans.

Digging Deeper

Did all the tobacco cans collect the same amount of water? Where was the most water collected? the least? Does distance from the sprinkler affect the amount of water collected? Is there any pattern to the way the water is spread by your sprinkler?

Would the result be the same if the sprinkler ran for a longer period of time? a shorter period of time?

How would the result be affected by a windy day?

Branching Out

How even is the distribution of water by other sprinklers?

Which sprinkler that you tested spread water most evenly? Can you suggest some reasons why it did the best job?

Place the tobacco cans in various places around your house or school just before a rainstorm. Measure the rainfall in each can after the rain has stopped. Is the amount of rainfall even in all places?

HOW TO MAKE A RAINDROP COLLECTOR

The raindrop collector is a device that will help you to measure the size of raindrops or the size of waterdrops produced by your sprinkler. Fill the lid of a shoe box with sifted flour until it is level with the top edge of the lid.

Use a ruler to smooth the surface of the flour.

Allow raindrops or waterdrops from a

If too much water falls on the flour a sticky mess will result. You may have to repeat this activity a few times to get a good sampling of waterdrops.

sprinkler to fall on the flour for a few seconds.

Bring the collector indoors and allow the waterdrops in the flour to dry out and become hard to form pellets.

Once the pellets have dried, use the flour sifter to sift out the pellets.

Branching Out

Use the raindrop collector during a rainstorm to find out how the raindrops compare in size with waterdrops from a sprinkler.

Activity 7:

How does the size of water droplets produced by different sprinklers compare?

Place a sprinkler on an open lawn and turn the water on full.

Allow a reasonable number of waterdrops to fall into a raindrop collector.

After the waterdrops have dried sift the pellets out of the waterdrop collector and sort them according to size. They can be held in place by putting them in order of size on the sticky surface of a strip of Scotch tape. Place a label on the Scotch tape to identify the sprinkler which produced the waterdrops.

Repeat these steps with the other sprinklers.

Compare the waterdrops produced by the sprinklers.

Digging Deeper

Which sprinkler produced the largest waterdrops? the smallest?

Which sprinkler would you use on a newly seeded lawn? Why?

Activity 8:

Is the ground under a bush as wet as the ground in an open lawn after watering?

Place a sprinkler so that it can water an area that includes open lawn, bushes, and evergreen shrubs.

Place a number of tobacco cans so that some are in the open area, some under bushes and some at the edge of bushes.

Water the area for an hour.

How does a bush affect the amount of rain that reaches the ground?

Turn off the water. With the rain gauge, measure the amount of water in each tobacco can. Carefully dig a number of places in the lawn and under shrubs and bushes to discover how deeply the water has penetrated into the ground.

Digging Deeper

Compare the amount of water that fell on the open lawn, under an evergreen shrub and at the edge of a bush. Where did the most fall? the least? Why?

How abundant is the plant life under the bushes? Why might one say that the climate under a bush can be much like a desert?

What results would you find if the sprinkler was turned on for 2 hours?

Branching Out

Repeat the activity during a rainfall. How do these results compare with those obtained when using a sprinkler?

Slopes, Grades and Gutters

3

3. Slopes, Grades and Gutters

Rain is a phenomenon with which all of us are acquainted. Since early childhood we can remember the various ways in which rain has fallen — from short heavy summer storms accompanied by violent claps of thunder and dazzling streaks of lightning to gentle drizzles extending over a period of several days. It is such a common occurrence that we tend to take it for granted, even though the water provided by rain is vital for recreation, industry, transportation, electricity and personal use.

Those who have studied rain know that water is never really wasted. It moves in a continuous cycle as shown in the diagram of the Water Cycle.

In this chapter we will look at some of the methods devised by man to control the run-off created by falling rain in our towns. Even before man changed the environment, nature occasionally experienced difficulties in dispersing rainwater — through absorption by the ground and gradual run-off. Today the drainage of rainwater in our towns and cities poses interesting problems because so much of the ground surface has been covered with a layer of concrete, asphalt and buildings through which the rainwater cannot pass. Often natural water courses such as streams and rivers have been filled in or rerouted. Since rainwater runs off paved surfaces as much as ten times faster than off unpaved land, man must improvise techniques to avoid flooding.

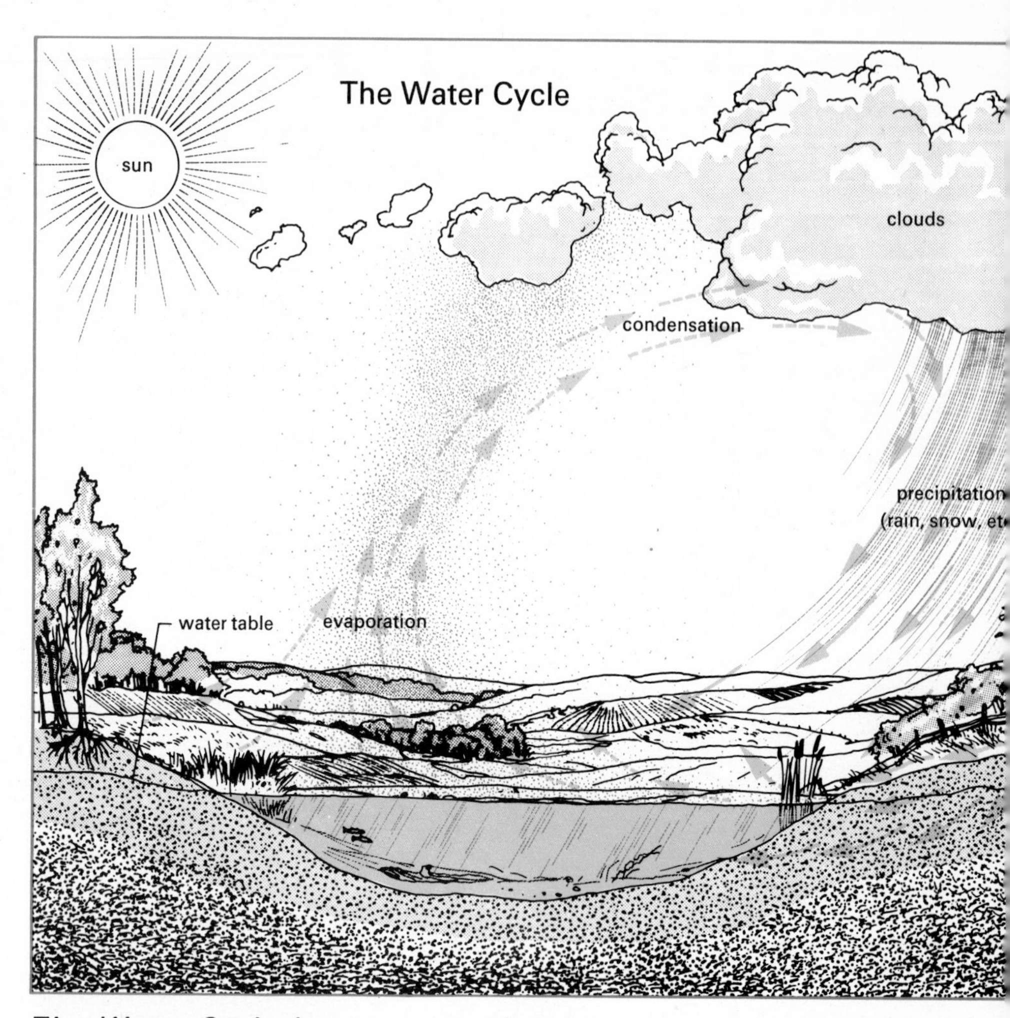

The Water Cycle is a process that is going on continuously throughout the world. The sun's energy evaporates water from oceans, lakes, rivers, streams and land surfaces. Plants give off water during the process of growth (transpiration). The water vapour that rises forms clouds of water droplets (condensation) which fall as precipitation (rain, snow, hail). Precipitation soaks into the soil (ground water), runs off the ground surface and flows to the sea. Some water is used by plants. Evaporation takes place again.

What problems might arise because the water is draining from the downspouts in this manner?

The roof of a building is designed to shed rainwater. During a rainfall the water from the roof can run down the sides of the building and discolour the paint or brick. By seeping through the brickwork or wood it can rot beams and ruin the inside walls. When it strikes the ground, it can dig holes in flower beds and wash away soil. The water that is absorbed into the ground can gather in the basement or keep the foundation of the building continually damp. Therefore a system of gutters (eavestroughs) and downspouts must be installed to protect a building from these hazards.

Activity 1:

Where are eavestroughs (gutters) located on buildings?

Select a building that has eavestroughs. Draw a sketch of the building showing clearly the location of the eavestroughs and downspouts.

Compare your building with those drawn by other students in your class.

Can you detect the slant of the eavestrough on this building?

Digging Deeper

Are eavestroughs found on all sides of all buildings?

Where are the eavestroughs located on a building?

Do flat roofed buildings have eavestroughs? How is rainwater carried away from flat roofed buildings?

Why do downspouts often end on a slab of concrete or on the lawn?

Branching Out

Of what material are eavestroughs made?
Visit a hardware store to see the parts of an eavestrough and downspout system. Ask the man at the store to name the parts and show you how they are fitted together.
What are *flashings*? What purpose do they serve?

Activity 2:

How are eavestroughs placed in order to speed the flow of water?

Examine the eavestroughs on a house and observe whether they are completely level or if they are placed on a slant.

Place a carpenter's level on the eavestroughs to determine if they are level. Choose eavestroughs that are quite close to the ground. If you use a ladder make certain that it is properly positioned and steady. Pour water into an eavestrough to find the direction in which it will flow.

On a sketch of the house showing the eavestroughs and downspouts, use

Damage resulting from faulty eavestrough systems.

Look for unusual arrangements of eavestroughs and downspouts as shown in the photographs. Find the reasons for the arrangements.

arrows to show the direction in which water will flow during a rainstorm.

Digging Deeper

How would the carpenter's level show a level eavestrough? a slanted eavestrough?

In what direction do the eavestroughs slant? Why?

Do all eavestroughs slant the same amount?

How many downspouts can you find on the house?

What would happen if the eavestroughs were slanted in the wrong direction?

Branching Out

Where does the water from the downspouts go? What are *cisterns* and *dry wells*? Where are they used?

Calculate the amount of water that must be carried away by the eavestroughs and downspouts of a house during a 2 inch rainfall.

Look for signs of damage, such as those listed in the introduction, on or around buildings where eavestroughs are lacking or not functioning properly.

Examine some eavestroughs in the autumn. Why should leaves and other debris be removed from them?

If the drainage from an eavestrough is poor, water will sit in it for long periods of time. What effect would this have on the durability of the eavestrough? Would mosquitoes breed in the water?

Find the eavestroughs on these cars. Why are there no eavestroughs at the front of the car?

Activity 3:

Do cars have eavestroughs?

Examine a variety of cars in a parking lot and along the street. Do all cars have eavestroughs?
Where are the eavestroughs located?
How are they different from the eavestroughs on houses?
Why do cars have eavestroughs?

Activity 4:

What differences can be found in the pitch or slope of the roofs of houses?

Select a block in your school area that includes houses that vary in age, size and style.
Use an angle finding device to measure the angle of slope or pitch for each roof in the block. You should work in groups and take an average of at least three readings for each roof.

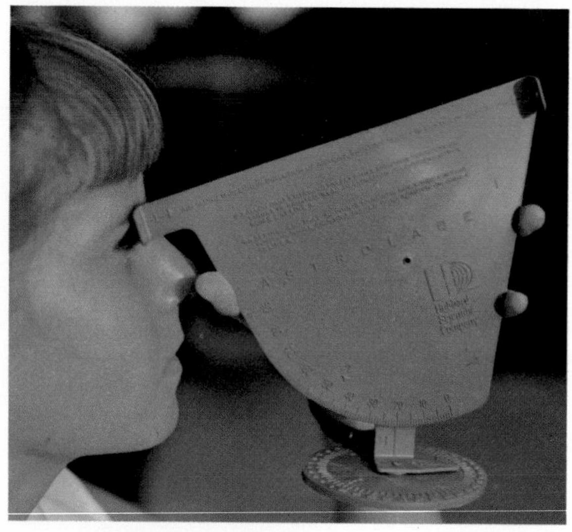

Angle finding devices that can be purchased.

HOW TO MAKE A SIMPLE ANGLE FINDING DEVICE

Glue a piece of wood 10″ x 1″ x ¾″ to the centre of a circular protractor. The edge of the wood should be parallel to a line connecting the 90 degree and 270 degree marks.
Push a thumb tack into the centre of the protractor.
Attach a heavy weight to a strong thread and tie the thread to the thumb tack.

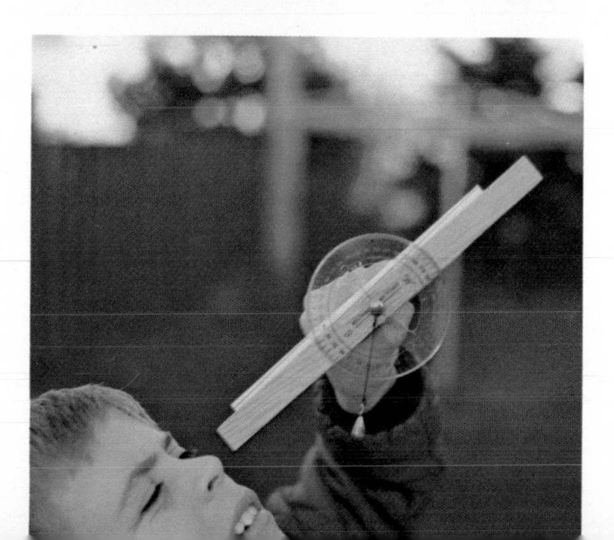

An improvised angle finder. Sight along the nails. A partner reads the slope of the roof on the protractor.

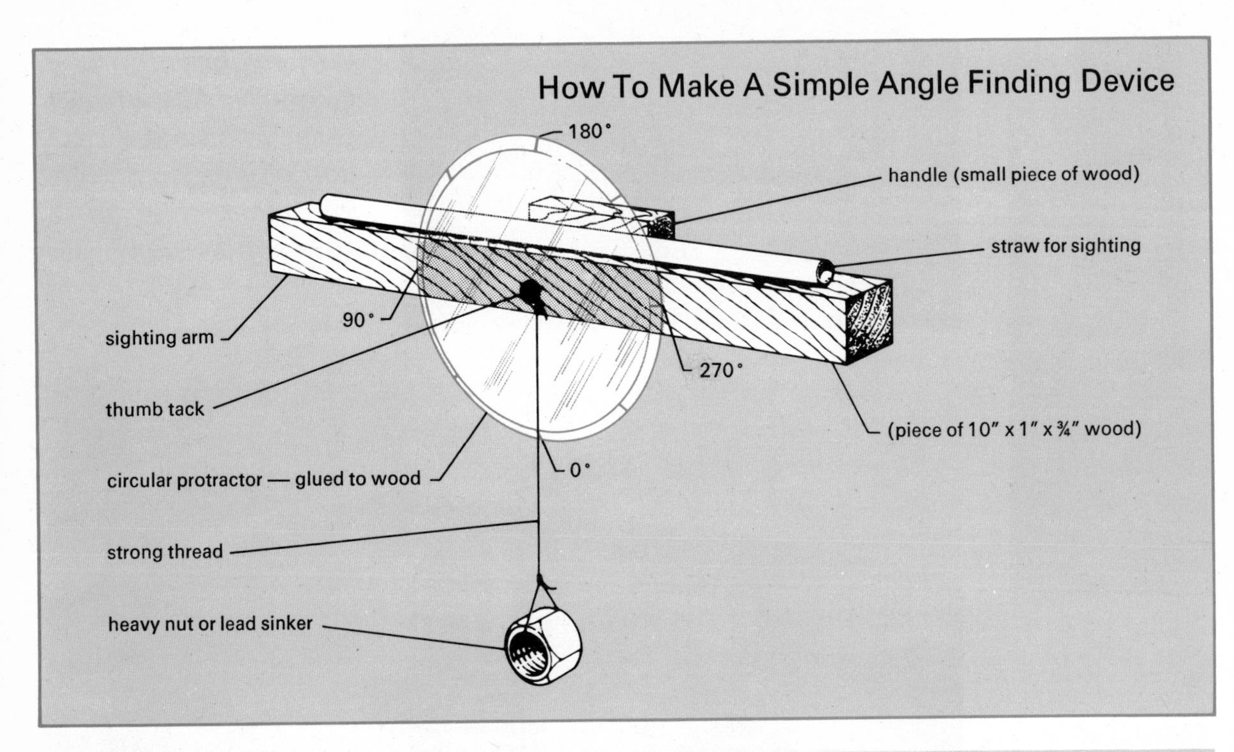

Differences in Roof Pitch

Block

			Slope of Roof			
Street	Address	Estimated age of house in years	First Reading	Second Reading	Third Reading	Average

When the piece of wood is held horizontally the thread should indicate 0 degrees.
Glue a plastic drinking straw onto the piece of wood for sighting.
Another small piece of wood can be glued to the sighting arm to act as a handle.

Record your information on a chart like the one shown.

Digging Deeper

What was the greatest pitch of roof? the least?
How did the roof pitch of old and new houses compare? What was the average pitch of the three oldest houses? the three newest houses?
Was there any difference in roof pitch between one-storey and two-storey houses?

Branching Out

Sketch the different roof styles that you observed. How many different styles did you notice? How many houses had the same style of roof? Make a study of the changes in buildings in your community over the past 100 years.

What materials are used for roofing? From where does roofing material come? Do people in all parts of the world use the same roofing materials? How are asphalt shingles made? Write to a manufacturer for information.

How are shingles laid to prevent water from entering the roof?

Would shingles from a roof with a great pitch or from a roof with a slight pitch be most easily damaged by a high wind? On a very windy day look for evidence to support your answer. How does the wind damage the shingles? Why would a roof with a considerable pitch be desirable in an area of heavy snowfall?

Why might you find a greater variety of roof styles in an older section of your community rather than in a new subdivision?

Activity 5:

Where are drains found?

Survey your school, both inside and out, to find the location of drains.

How many can you find? Where are the drains found?

Use a carpenter's level or a steel ball bearing, which will roll easily, to discover how the ground or floor surface around a drain slopes.

What is the farthest distance from which a ball bearing or marble will roll toward the drain?

An inside and an outside drain.

Finding the way in which the floor surface slopes around a drain.

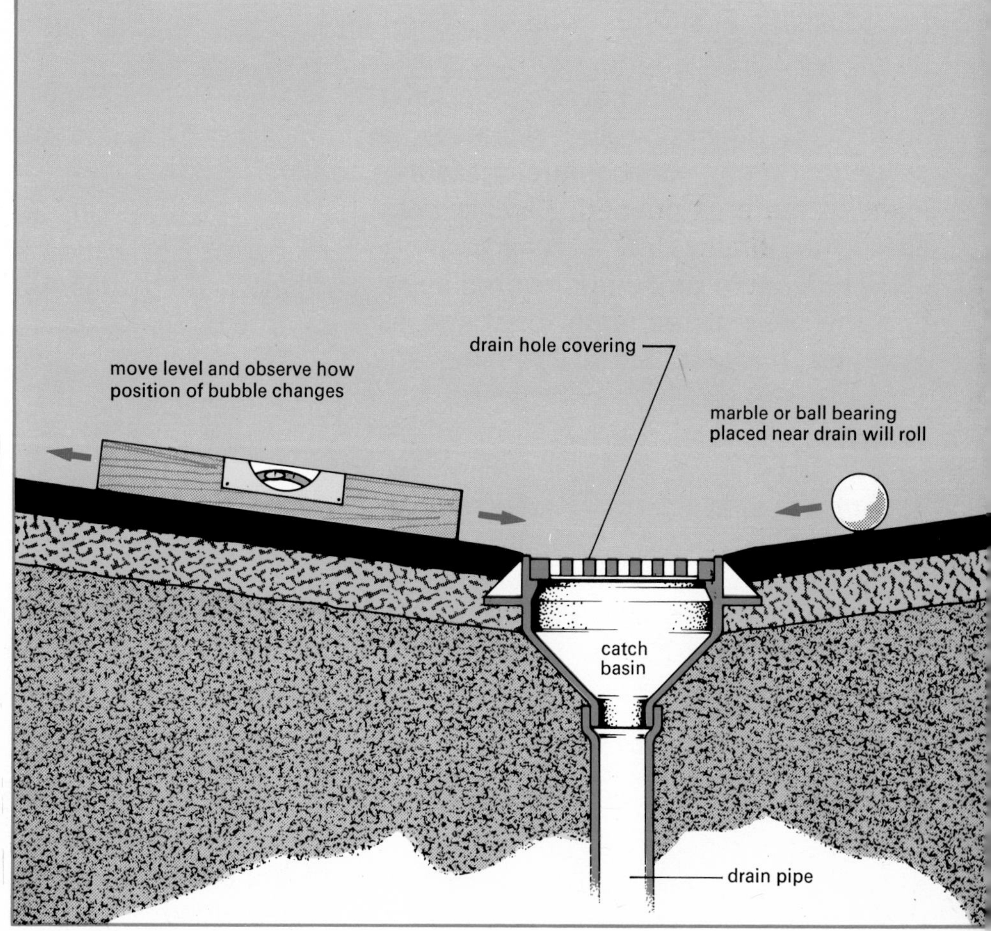

Digging Deeper

Where does the water that enters a drain go?
Provide a reason for the location of each drain that you found.
Why do water puddles form in some basements?

Activity 6:

How large an area is drained by a drain?

Use a watering can or pail of water to find from what distance water will travel to reach a drain. Work with the caretaker if you are trying this activity inside the school. Water will have to be poured from many directions and distances in order to obtain an accurate measurement of the area drained. Always pour toward the drain. Only a small quantity of water should be poured each time so that the path of the water as it moves along a surface can be easily seen.

These students have poured pails of water to find the greatest distances from which water will run to the drain.

Prepare a scale map showing the area drained and the location of the drain.

Find a reasonable number of points that show the maximum distance of drainage. Connect these points with a suitable line.

A map showing area drained and location of drain.

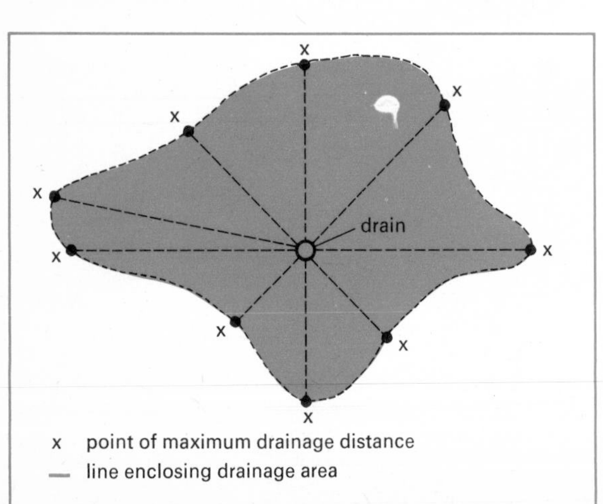

Digging Deeper

How do you know when you have located a point of maximum drainage distance from the drain?
Is a drain always in the centre of the area being drained?
Where is the drain in the basement of your house located? Why? Are all parts of the basement of your house equally well drained?

Activity 7:

How are road surfaces designed for good drainage?

Stretch a string tightly, so there is no sag, from curb to curb across a street. Be sure to select a street that has little traffic. One or two students should be stationed to watch for traffic and to warn the group when cars are approaching.

With a ruler, measure the distance from the string to the road surface at intervals of 2 feet.

Prepare a scale drawing on graph paper to illustrate the data that you collected.

Digging Deeper

How much higher is the road at the centre than at the curb?

How does the design of the road surface promote good drainage?

Do all roads have the same slope?

Why do old roads frequently drain poorly?

Interview the city engineer or a contractor engaged in road building for more information about drainage in road construction.

Activity 8:

Where are catch basins (drains along the gutters of a street) located on the street?

Prepare a map of an area near your school to show the location of the catch basins.

Why does this road slope towards the curbs?

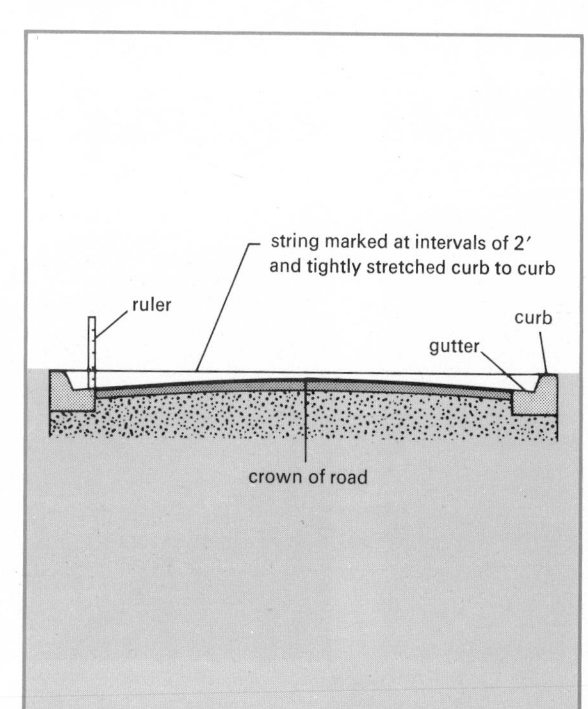

Road surfaces are designed for good drainage.

At various points along the curb, pour pails of water into the gutter to find the direction in which water flows.

Use coloured arrows on your map to show the direction of water flow.

Digging Deeper

What evidence did you find of careful engineering to permit easy drainage of water to the catch basins?

Why do roads sometimes flood even though catch basins are present?

Why are catch basins usually found in pairs on opposite sides of the street?

Branching Out

Where does the water entering a catch basin go?

On your map showing the location of catch basins indicate where the connecting pipes that carry away rainwater might be found. How can you find out if you are right?

On many streets you will find manhole covers. What are some of the reasons for the manholes?

Activity 9:

What other efforts to promote good drainage can be found around the home and school?

Use a carpenter's level to find as many examples as possible around the house and school where efforts have been made to encourage water to flow away from the building. Some of the areas that should be investigated are window ledges, sidewalks, driveways, doorsills.

List all of the examples that you found and beside each place your assumption of what might happen if these efforts to provide good drainage were neglected.

The catch basin at a street corner.

Finding the slope of a doorsill.

Moving the Earth 4

4. Moving the Earth

What is the *population explosion*? It is a threat potentially more dangerous than a bomb. Newspapers and other news media are making us aware of man's growing concern about rapidly increasing population. The world population of approximately three billion in 1960 is expected to double to six billion by the year 2000. Over fifty million additional human beings must be fed each year.

To many people of the affluent countries, plagued with food surpluses, it is hard to accept the warnings of imminent world-wide food shortage and famine. Even now, however, millions of people throughout the world are suffering from inadequate or insufficient food. What will be the situation in the year 2000?

Productive soil is the basis of most of our food supply. Regardless of population, the size of our planet will remain the same. The amount of land available for food production will not increase appreciably. In fact, just the opposite is taking place. Large acreages are lost to food production each year by the expansion of cities, highways, etc. Many acres now under cultivation should be reforested because they are unsuitable for agriculture. Most important, much of our best farmland has been destroyed or damaged by erosion resulting from poor farming practices. Our very survival makes it vital that we learn more about this problem and take appropriate action.

Most soil erosion is caused by running water. The picture at the beginning of this chapter shows a vivid example of soil erosion. Perhaps you have seen many similar examples in your community. This chapter suggests a number of simple activities that will make you more aware of the beginnings of soil erosion around your house and school.

Activity 1:

How quickly do soils absorb water?

Soils vary in their ability to absorb water. During a heavy rainstorm soils that cannot absorb the rainwater quickly cause the water to run off. As the water runs over the surface it picks up particles of soil and deposits them elsewhere. The water that runs off flows into streams, lakes, and oceans and so cannot be used by plants later on. The soil that remains is less fertile because some of the richer topsoil has been washed away.

Obtain six tin cans that are the same size. Soft drink cans are ideal.

Remove the top and bottom from five of the cans. Place a mark on each of the five cans, ½ inch from a rim.

Press a can ½ inch deep (use the mark as a guide) into each of the following soils:

(a) clay or clay loam such as might be found around a construction site
(b) sandy soil such as in a sand or jumping pit
(c) rich garden soil
(d) lawn where the grass is growing well
(e) heavily trampled path on a lawn.

Use the sixth can to pour a full can of water into each of the others.

Testing the ability of a lawn to absorb water.

This activity should be done on the same day so that you can be reasonably sure that the amount of water in each type of soil is, to some extent, the same.

Start timing the rate of absorption as soon as you start to pour the water. Stop timing when no more water remains in the can. In some soils you should be prepared for a long wait.

Record for each can, the location, the appearance of the soil (size of particles, texture, ingredients, etc.) and the time required for the water to be absorbed by the ground. Show the times on a bar graph.

Digging Deeper

Which soil absorbed water the fastest? the slowest?

Which soil would produce run-off most easily?

What factors seemed to contribute to the rapid absorption of water by soil?

Branching Out

Test and compare the rate of absorption for other soils. You might try under a shrub, a woodland area and along a fence row. Can you think of other places? Be certain that the areas you select contain clear differences in soil.

Test concrete and asphalt surfaces (sidewalks, driveways) for absorption. Since the cans cannot be pressed into these surfaces press plasticene around the lower rim of the can to prevent the water from escaping. How does concrete and asphalt compare with soil in the ability to absorb water?

Activity 2:

How does the force of falling raindrops affect the soil?

Before soil erosion can take place the soil particles must be loosened.

Falling raindrops have considerable force. As they strike the ground surface they break up the soil and splash small particles into the air. These particles of soil can be easily carried away by run-off water. The amount of splash erosion can be measured.

Obtain three one-quart cardboard milk cartons.

Anchor the containers securely by half filling each with stones.

Use elastic bands to secure a piece of white paper around each container.

Before a rain place one container on bare soil, another in a vegetable or flower garden and the third on a grassy lawn.

After the rain compare the soil splash marks showing on the white paper.

When the papers have dried they can be removed from the milk cartons and kept as a permanent record.

Digging Deeper

Which splash pillar had the most soil on it?

Which splash pillar had the highest splash marks on it?

On which side of each splash pillar were the most splashes found? Why?

Which location suffered most from splash erosion? the least?

What factors influenced the amount and height of the splash?

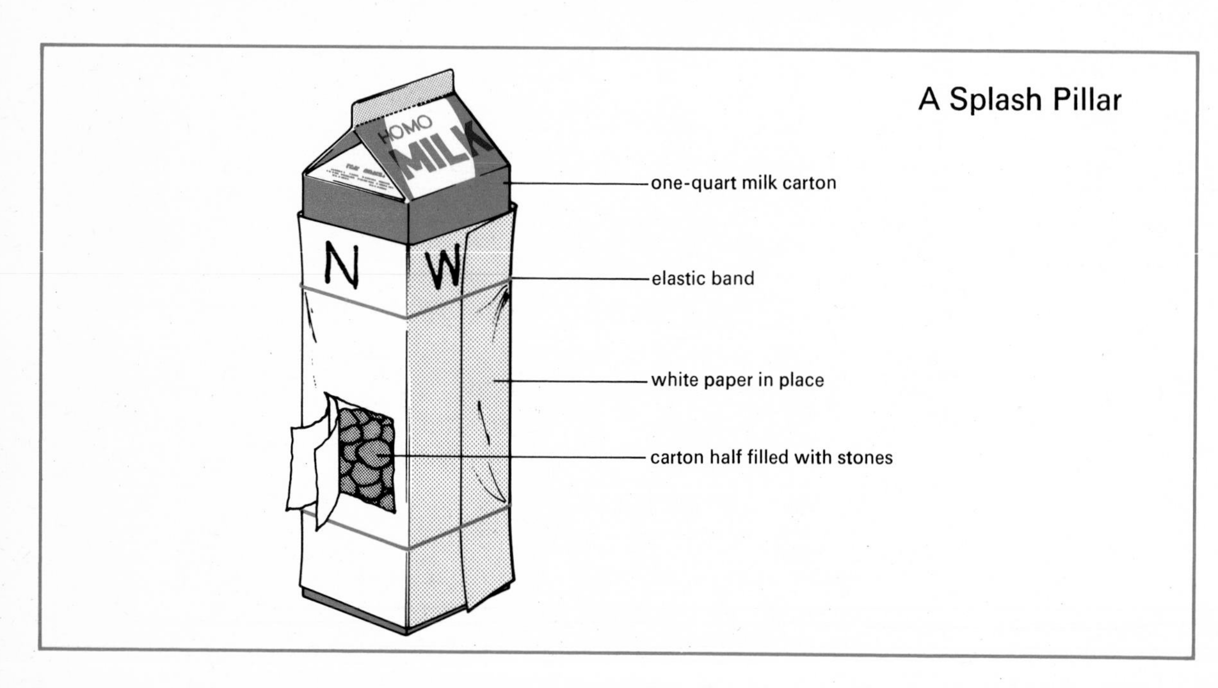

A milk carton surrounded by white paper makes a good splash pillar.

Branching Out

Place splash pillars in a number of other locations such as under trees and bushes and next to fences and buildings. Compare your findings with those already noted.
Use your splash pillars in the same areas during a light shower and during a heavy downpour. How do the results compare?
Use your splash pillars when your sprinkler is watering your lawn and garden.
How do the results compare with the results obtained during a rainfall?

Activity 3:

How do sheet erosion and gully erosion start?

On the playground or in a garden build a mound of soil about 2 feet high.

The soil should contain a good mixture of fine particles, lumps, plant remains and stones.

Pour water onto the mound from a watering can or from a hose partially turned on and adjusted to produce a fine spray. Continue to water until the height of the mound has been reduced by at least 6 inches.

Draw sketches to show a bird's-eye view of the mound and surrounding area, before and after watering.

Digging Deeper

How quickly did absorption of water by

How water can cause soil erosion.

the soil stop and puddling begin?

What colour were the puddles? What caused this discolouration?

What size of soil particles were carried off first by run-off?

What size of soil particles were carried farthest by run-off?

What materials were left behind?

When did little gullies start to appear on the mound?

What would be the effect of increasing the flow of water?

Explain what is meant by sheet erosion and gully erosion.

Branching Out

After a rain, look along sidewalks and in the gutters along the street for evidence of sheet erosion.

Find a small gully at a construction site or by a recently built road. Measure the rate of growth of the gully (increasing width, depth and length) after each rainfall over a period of time.

Activity 4:

How can running water be slowed down to reduce soil erosion?

Construct two wooden boxes each 20 inches long, 10 inches wide and 4 inches deep.

Obtain a watering can and two large, wide-mouthed bottles that will hold at least 1 quart.

Activity 4 (a):

How does plant cover affect erosion?

Cut a piece of sod from the lawn to fit one of the boxes. Be sure to ask permission to remove the sod, and take it from an inconspicuous spot. Trim the grass to a height of about 1 inch, with a pair of scissors, to make it easier to handle.

Fill the other box with bare soil from the same place.

Place the boxes on a table so that the spouts extend over the edge.

Raise the other end of the boxes by sliding a length of wood 1 inch thick under them.

Set the bottles under the spouts so that they can catch any water that runs out of the boxes.

Put 2 quarts of water in the watering can and then pour the water on one of the boxes at the end farthest from the bottle. Repeat this activity with the second box. Be careful to pour the water on both boxes at the same time, in the same way, and from the same height.

Note and record the following:

(a) how long it takes for water to start dripping from the spouts,
(b) the amount of water collected in each bottle,
(c) how long it takes for water to stop dripping from the spouts,
(d) the clarity of the water in each bottle.

Filter the water from the bottles to find the quantity of soil that eroded from each box.

10″
20″
4″
notch 1½″ deep
spout made from a tin can

A wooden box with a spout attached can be used to study soil erosion.

Finding the effect of plant cover on soil erosion.

Finding the effect of mulching on soil erosion.

Finding the effect of contouring on soil erosion.

Finding the effect of ground slope on soil erosion.

Digging Deeper

Why could this activity be called a *controlled experiment*? The one variable most difficult to control is the amount of moisture in the soil in each box at the beginning of the experiment. If the soil was too wet at the beginning you may have to repeat the activity using drier soil.

Explain in detail how a cover crop, such as grass, will control soil erosion.

How could cattle and sheep cause soil erosion on grassy land?

Activity 4(b):

How does mulching affect erosion?

Fill each box with the same type of soil. Cover one box with straw, sawdust, leaves, grass or wood shavings. This is called *mulching.* Repeat the steps and observations made in 4(a).

Explain how mulching will control soil erosion.

Activity 4(c):

How does contouring affect soil erosion?

Fill each box with the same type of soil. Using your finger, make furrows going crosswise in one box and lengthwise in the other. Repeat the steps and observations made in 4(a).

What is contouring? Explain how contouring will control soil erosion.

Activity 4(d):

What types of soil are most easily eroded?

Fill one box with poor, sandy soil. Fill the other with good, garden soil rich in *humus* (decayed plant material). Repeat the steps and observations made in 4(a).

Which soil eroded least? Try other soil samples and compare the results.

How does humus help to reduce soil erosion?

Activity 4(e):

How does the slope of the ground affect soil erosion?

Fill each box with the same type of soil. Raise the end of one box 1 inch and the other 3 inches. Repeat the steps and observations made in 4(a).

Repeat this experiment with boxes raised 2 inches and 5 inches. How is soil erosion affected as the slope is increased? Why should steeply sloping land not be farmed? What should be done with this land?

Branching Out

Find the slope of the land on your school ground and other places in your community. Slope is measured in percent. If, over a distance of 100 inches the land rises or falls 1 inch, the slope is 1 percent.

You will need a yardstick, a straight stick 50 inches long and a carpenter's level.
Fasten the level to the stick with elastic bands. Place one end of the stick so that it touches the ground. Raise the other end until the bubble on the carpenter's level shows that the stick is perfectly level. Use the yardstick to measure the distance from the end of the stick to the ground. Multiply the answer by two to obtain the percent of slope.
If the yardstick shows a rise of 3 inches, what is the percent of slope?

Measuring the slope of the ground around a house.

Bibliography

1. Bale, Robert O. *Conservation for Camp and Classroom.* Minneapolis: Burgess Publishing Co., 1966.

2. *Better Homes and Gardens Handyman's Book.* Des Moines: Meredith Publishing Co., 1951.

3. Blough, G. O., and Schwartz, J. *Elementary School Science and How to Teach It.* New York: Holt, Rinehart and Winston, 1964.

4. Brinkhurst, Ralph O., and Chant, Donald A. *This Good, Good Earth: our fight for survival.* Toronto: MacMillan Co. of Canada, Ltd., 1971.

5. Brown, R. E., and Mouser, G. W. *Techniques for Teaching Conservation Education.* Minneapolis: Burgess Publishing Co., 1966.

6. Cram, J. S. *Water — Canadian Needs and Resources.* Montreal: Harvest House, Ltd., 1968.

7. Hammersley, A.; Jones, E.; and Perry, G. A. *Approaches to Environmental Studies — Teachers' Guide Book 1.* Blandford Press, Ltd., 1968.

8. Hone, A.; Joseph, A.; and Victor, E. *Teaching Elementary Science: A Sourcebook for Elementary Science.* New York: Harcourt, Brace & World, Inc., 1962.

9. Hug, J. W., and Wilson, P. J. *Curriculum Enrichment Outdoors.* New York: Harper & Row, Publishers, 1965.

10. Leopold, L. B., and Davis, K. S. *Water — Life Science Library.* New York: Time Inc., 1966.

11. Lowry, W. P. *Weather and Life.* New York: Academic Press, 1969.

12. McCoy, J. J. *Shadows Over the Land.* New York: The Seabury Press, 1970.

13. *Nuffield Junior Science—Teacher's Guide 2.* Collins Clear-Type Press, 1967.

14. Overman, Michael. *Water.* Garden City, N.Y.: Doubleday & Co., Inc., 1969.

15. *Popular Science Do-it-Yourself Encyclopedia.* Arlich Publishing Co., 1956.

16. Reiner, Laurence E. *Methods and Materials of Construction.* New Jersey: Prentice-Hall, Inc., 1970.

17. *Science Year.* The World Book Science Annual. Chicago: Field Enterprises Educational Corp., 1971.

18. Sheffe, Norman. *Environmental Quality.* Toronto: McGraw-Hill of Canada, Ltd., 1971.

Glossary

Blueprint: A photographic print of a drawing, white lines on a blue background, used as a plan in building operations, etc.

Cistern: A tank for storing rainwater.

Clay loam: A soil mixture heavy with clay.

Condensation: The changing of vapour into a liquid.

Contouring: Ploughing crosswise to a slope.

Controlled experiment: A carefully conducted experiment that allows one to compare the effect of one variable.

Drain: A pipe for carrying away water.

Dry well: A pit filled with gravel into which rainwater can run and eventually seep away.

Erosion: Washing away of soil.

Filter: A device, such as a paper towel, tea towel, or filter paper, used to separate solids from liquids.

Flashing: Pieces of metal used to cover the joints of a building to make them watertight.

Flexible: Yielding to stress without breaking.

Hard water: Water with a considerable amount of minerals dissolved in it.

Irrigation: The artificial watering of land by means of sprinkling, ditches, etc.

Loam: A soil which contains clay, silt, fine sand, and humus.

Mulching: Covering the ground with straw, grass, sawdust, leaves, etc.

Pitch: The slope or slant.

Plumber: A man who puts in and repairs water pipes.

Precipitation: Moisture falling from the clouds or separating from the air, such as rain, snow, sleet, hail, fog, frost.

Pumper: A type of fire engine.

Rain gauge: A device for measuring the amount of rainfall.

Septic system: A method of dealing with sewage from a single house.

Soft water: Water that is relatively free from mineral salts.

Truck farm: A farm where garden vegetables are raised for market.

Variable: A changeable factor in an experiment.

Washer: A disk of metal, leather, fibre, or rubber used to make a watertight closure.

Water pressure: The force of water.

Water table: The level below which ground (porous rock) is saturated with water.

Index of Activities

Chapter 3 Slopes, Grades and Gutters *29*

Activity 1: *Page 31*

Where are eavestroughs (gutters) located on buildings?

Activity 2: *Page 32*

How are eavestroughs placed in order to speed the flow of water?

Activity 3: *Page 34*

Do cars have eavestroughs?

Activity 4: *Page 34*

What differences can be found in the pitch or slope of the roofs of houses?

Activity 5: *Page 37*

Where are drains found?

Activity 6: *Page 38*

How large an area is drained by a drain?

Activity 7: *Page 39*

How are road surfaces designed for good drainage?

Activity 8: *Page 39*

Where are catch basins (drains along the gutters of a street) located?

Activity 9: *Page 40*

What other efforts to promote good drainage can be found around the home and school?

Chapter 4 Moving the Earth *41*

Activity 1: *Page 42*

How quickly do soils absorb water?

Activity 2: *Page 44*

How does the force of falling raindrops affect the soil?

Activity 3: *Page 45*

How do sheet erosion and gully erosion start?

Activity 4: *Page 46*

How can running water be slowed down to reduce soil erosion?

Activity 4 (a): *Page 46*

How does plant cover affect erosion?

Activity 4 (b): *Page 49*

How does mulching affect erosion?

Activity 4 (c): *Page 49*

How does contouring affect soil erosion?

Activity 4 (d): *Page 49*

What types of soil are most easily eroded?

Activity 4 (e): *Page 49*

How does the slope of the ground affect soil erosion?